CW01045399

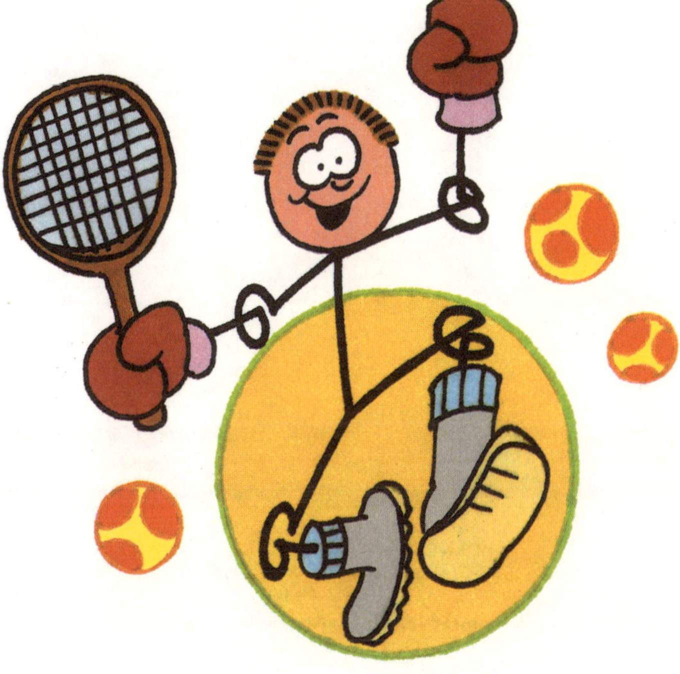

Carnival
An imprint of the Children's Division
of the Collins Publishing Group
8 Grafton St, London W1X 3LA

Published by Collins in Association with
Oxford Graphics Limited 1989
Characters and illustrations copyright © Liza and David Mostyn 1989
Storyline text copyright © Ann Loescher 1989
The Sprongs is a trademark.

ISBN 0 00 194920 9

All rights reserved.

Printed and bound in Great Britain by
The Eagle Press Plc, Glasgow

The Sprongs™ Play Jelly Tennis

Ann Loescher

Illustrations by David Mostyn

Series Editor Liza Mostyn

Of course you know that the Sprongs bounce and leap about and go places at great speed. But do you know that Bendy is the bouncingest, leapingest, fastest Sprong of them all? Well, he is.

One day when Bendy was tidying the loft he found two tennis rackets and a ball. He forgot all about tidying and hurried down the stairs and out into the garden.

He held a racket in each hand and bounced the ball from one to the other. It didn't take him long to realise that it would be much more fun to play tennis with someone else.

"Oh dear, no net!" he said to himself out loud. Then he ran to the kitchen and returned with an armload of aprons. He tied them all together in a long line.

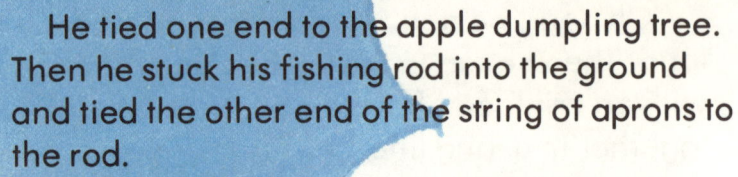

He tied one end to the apple dumpling tree. Then he stuck his fishing rod into the ground and tied the other end of the string of aprons to the rod.

"There," he said triumphantly. "A net!"

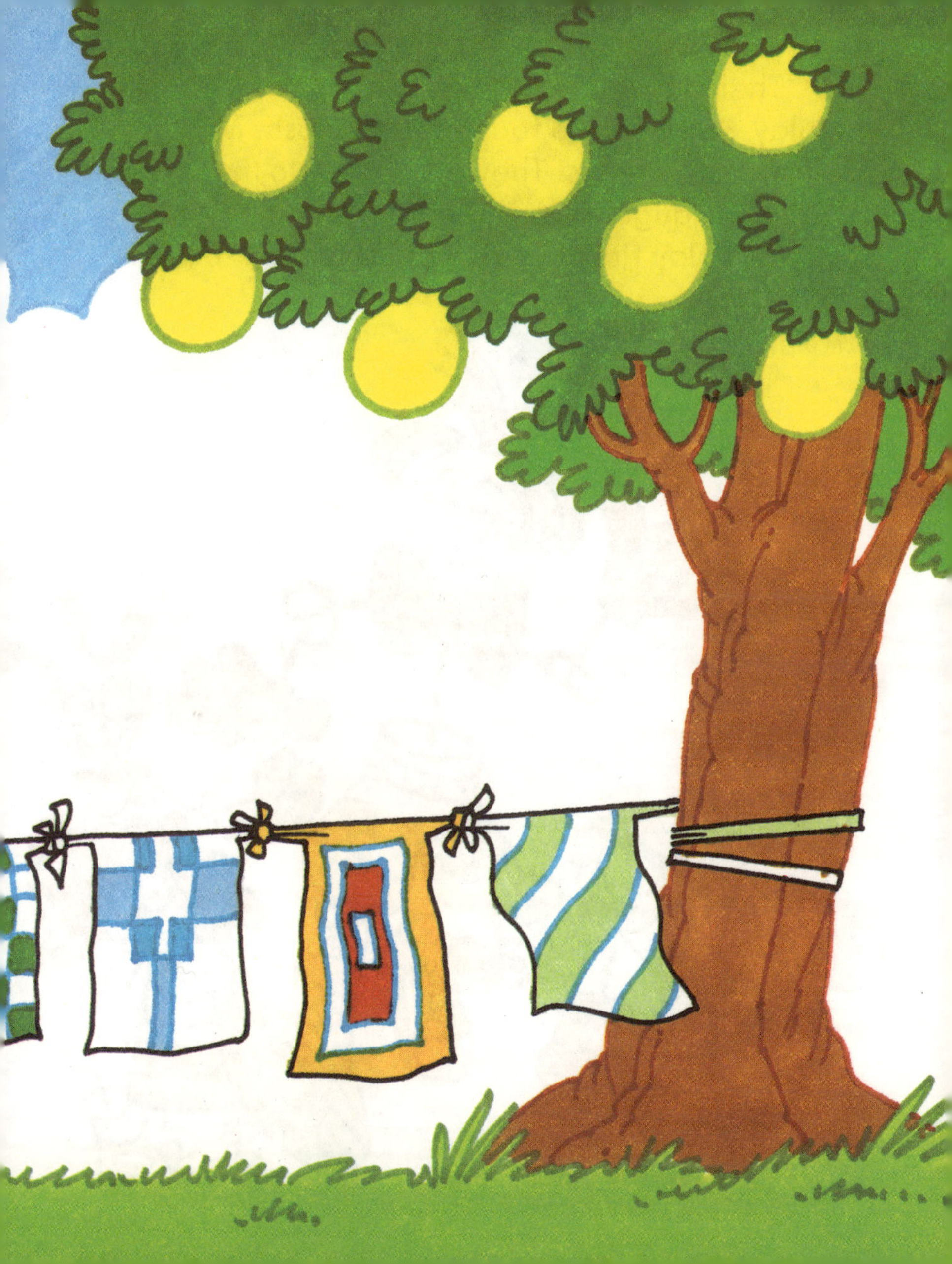

Then he went off to find a friend who would play with him. He found four: Splash, Minn, Trifle, and Suggs. They all came into the garden laughing and chattering.

"I'll play first. I'm very good at this," boasted Splash.

Splash played very well and he leapt about as quickly as any of the Sprongs — all except Bendy! Splash was no match for Bendy's speed and at last he gave up.

"It's my knee," he said making an excuse. "It has a kink in it."

Next Minn and Trifle decided to try together to beat Bendy. Minn used the racket and Trifle used a frying pan. It looked very silly and did not work at all well.

They crashed into each other and ended up in a terrible tangle. Their knees and elbows were all twisted together so that the others had to untangle them.

Then Suggs thought to himself, "If I hit the ball really hard it will go whizzing past Bendy so fast that he won't be able to hit it."

But Suggs hadn't realised just how fast Bendy was. The third time Suggs hit the ball he hit it so hard he bent the handle of the racket.

The four Sprong friends grumbled, "It's no fun playing with you. We're going." And off they went leaving Bendy feeling very sorry for himself because he was too good at something.

Bendy sulked for a while, bouncing the ball on his racket. Suddenly an idea struck him.
"I can play by myself!" he said.

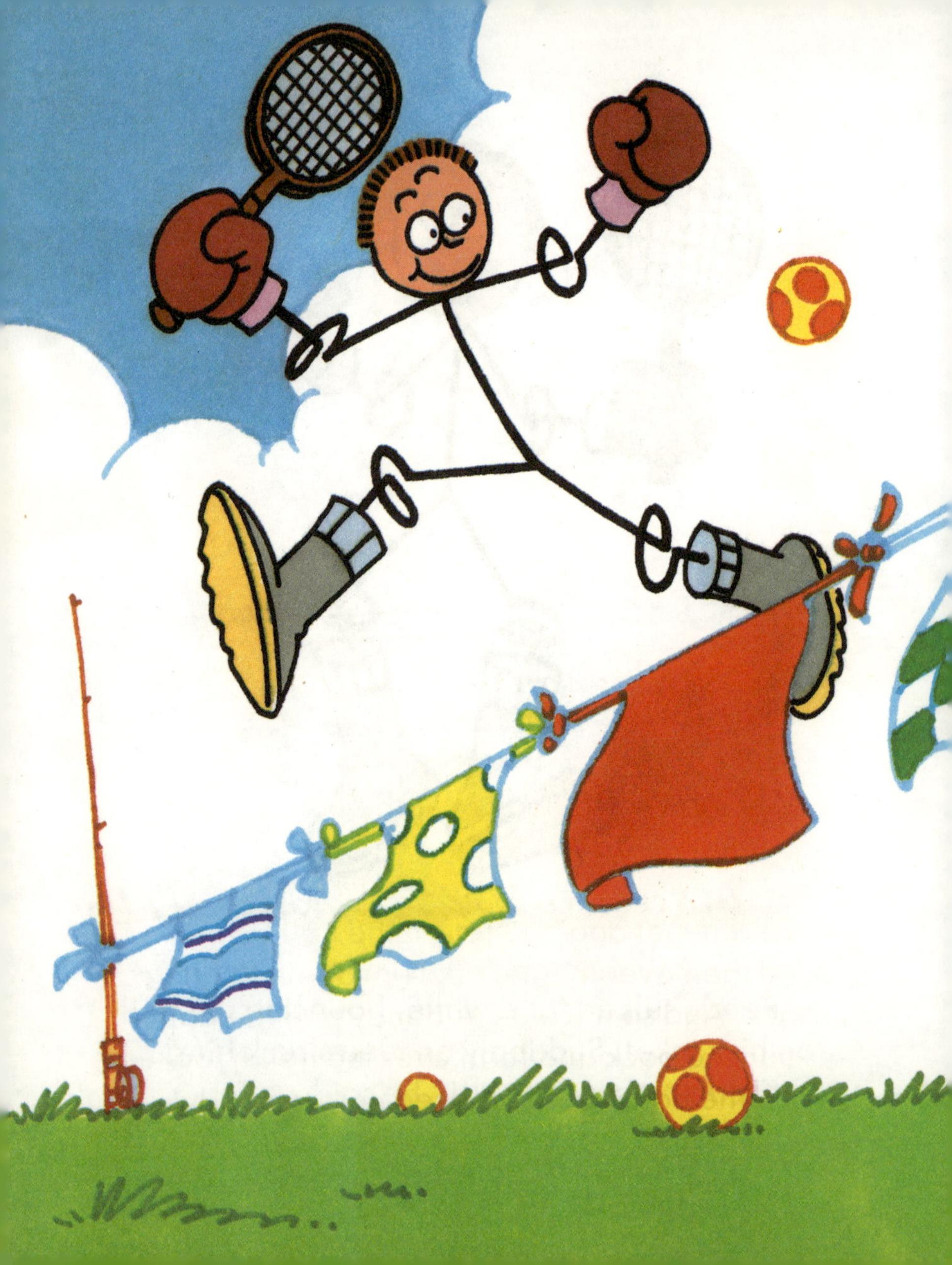

He swatted the ball over the net and leapt over the net in plenty of time to hit the ball back over again. Then of course he had to leap over the net again to return the ball to himself and then over the net he went again to hit it back. And so it went on, Bendy and the ball bounced back and forth over the net. It looked as if the ball would get tired before Bendy!

The score was even when Casey who was going past stopped to watch. "Why are you playing tennis by yourself?" he asked. Bendy told him the whole sad story.

"May I have a go?" asked Casey. He had only played with Bendy for less than a minute when he said, "You're just too good at this. You go too fast! We'll have to do something to slow you down and I've got just the idea. Have you got any jelly?"

"Yes," answered Bendy with a puzzled look. They went to the kitchen together and cooked up a huge amount of strawberry jelly.

"Get two buckets," said Casey.

Bendy, fast as ever, was back with the buckets in no time. Casey and Bendy filled the buckets with strawberry jelly. There was lots left over.

"Let's find anything we can that will hold the jelly!" said Casey.

Bendy went out to the shed and returned with an old wellington boot, a flower pot with a cork in the hole, an old bowler hat, a bird bath, and the cup he had won for growing giant blue marrows. Casey emptied the kitchen cupboards of all the bowls and pans and cups and teapots.

Together they poured the left-over jelly into all the things they had found and lined them up on the garden wall.

"We can invite all the Sprongs to help us eat this later," said Casey.

When the jelly in the buckets was almost firm, Casey plunked Bendy's feet into it. Of course the jelly overflowed onto the kitchen floor but Sprongs are very casual about things like that.

"Now stand very still until it sets," Casey warned Bendy.

Meanwhile Casey went around the neighbourhood calling out to all the Sprongs to come to the big tennis match at Bendy's house. "Anyone can play!" he shouted.

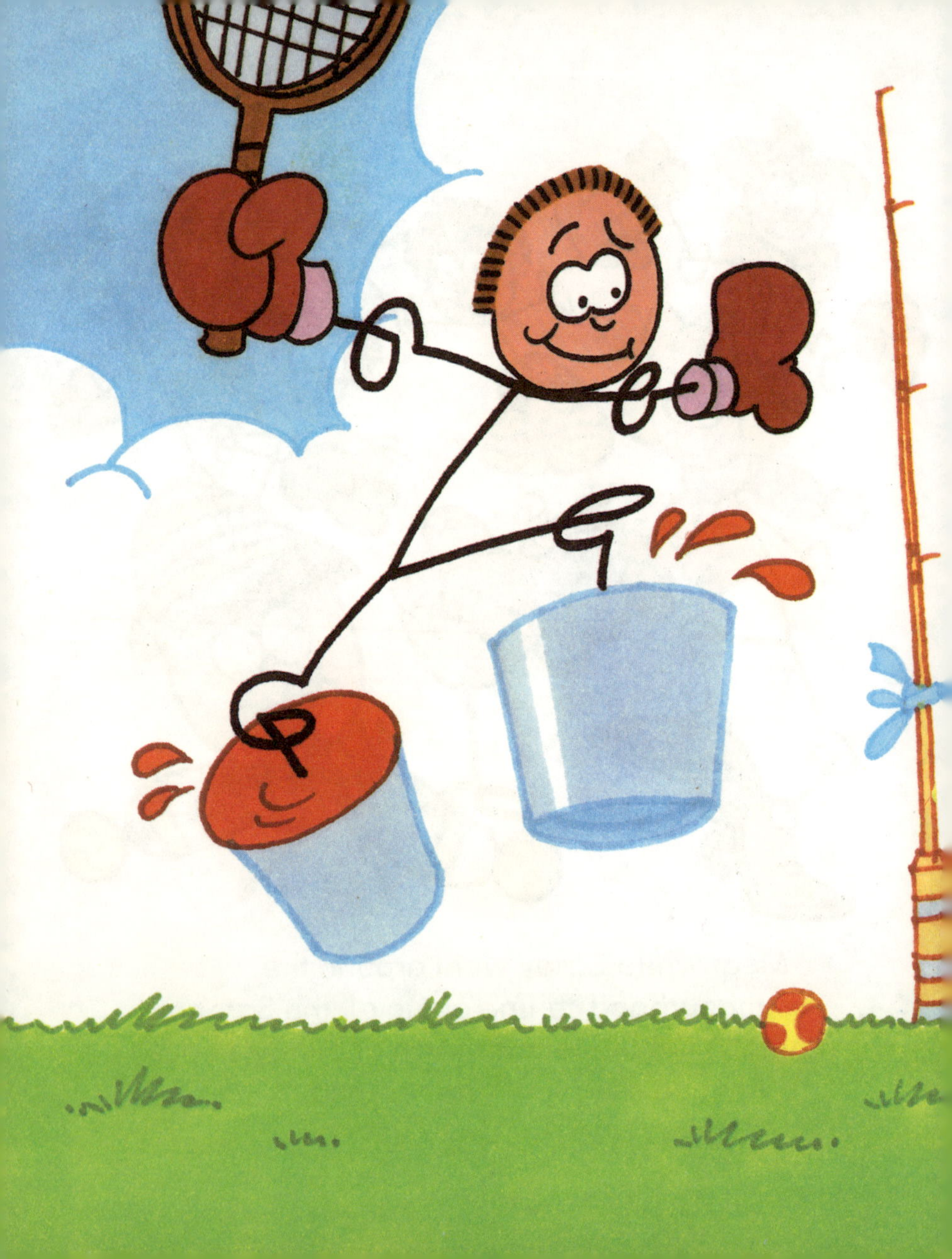

Before long the match was under way. As usual Bendy leapt about but he was so weighted down by the buckets of strawberry jelly that he could not go any faster than any other Sprong.

Everyone had a turn to play with Bendy. The other Sprongs shouted and yelled and cheered. Bendy played and played until he was too tired to move.

"Now, who's for strawberry jelly?" asked Casey.
   Bendy had worked the hardest so he got the big jelly welly!

Wall Ball

You will need a ball that you can hold in your hand. A tennis ball is just right.

Stand about 2-4 metres from the blind wall of a house or garage. The wall should be fairly flat and the surface that you stand on should be firm and flat too.

Use your open hand like a bat to smack the ball against the wall. Let it bounce once back toward you. Then hit it back to the wall. See how many volleys you can make without missing a hit.

Develops hand/eye coordination and stamina.

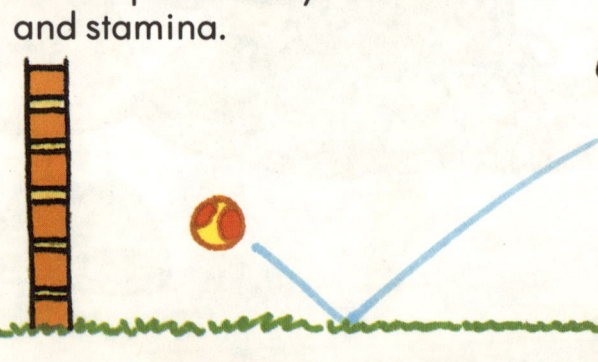

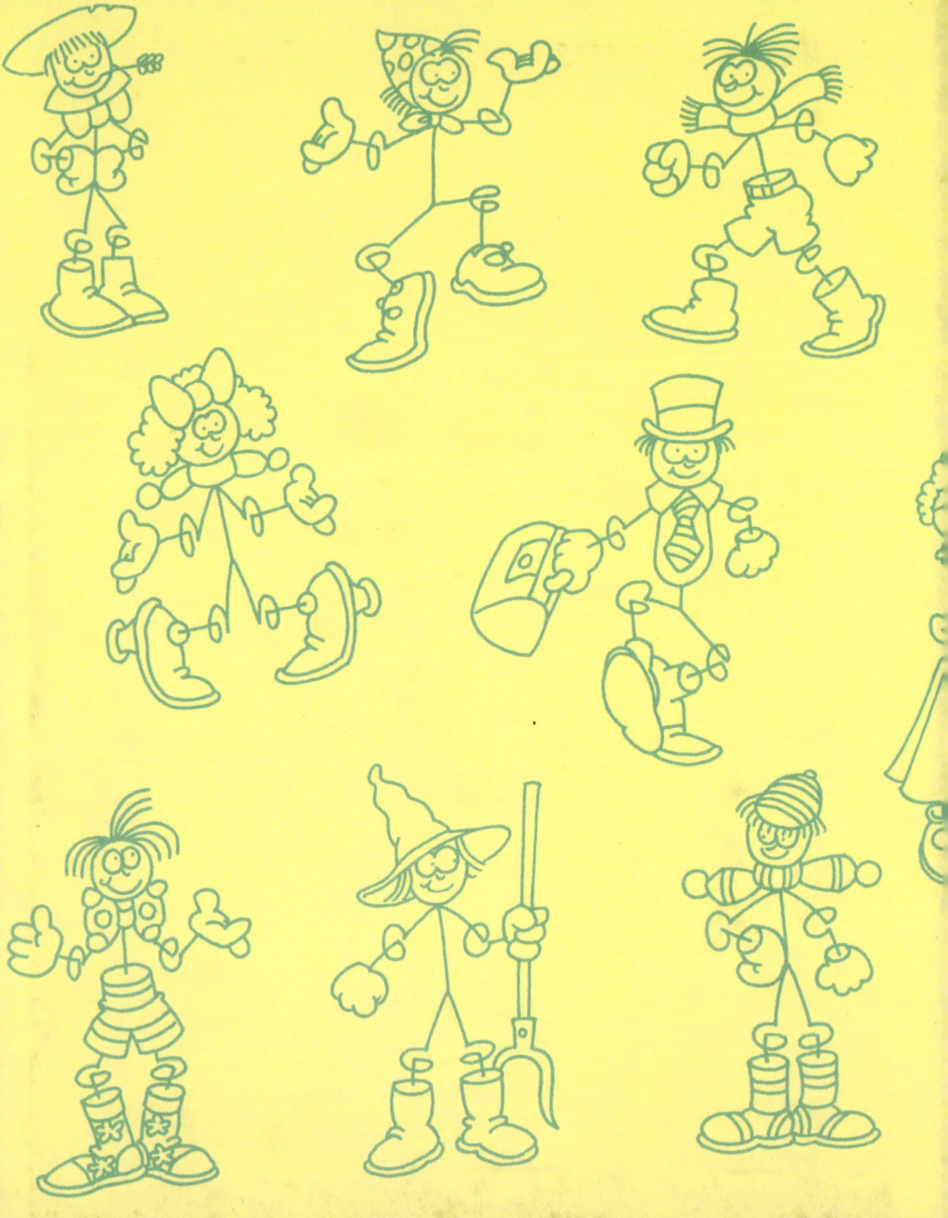

A Trip to Doctor Woof

A play by
Vivian French

Illustrated by
Andy Rowland

Characters

Doctor
(Dr Woof)

Dot

Nurse
(Nurse Ruff)

Mum

Nip

Pip

Nurse: Good morning, Mrs Bark! How are you today?

Mum: Good morning, Nurse. Please can Doctor Woof take a look at Dot?

Nurse: What is the matter with Dot today?

Pip: Dot has spots – lots and lots of spots!

Nip: Yes, she's got big red spots!

Dot: Can Doctor Woof help me?

Nurse: Let's see …

They go into Doctor Woof's room.

Doctor: Good morning, Dot. What is the matter with you?

Dot: I have lots and lots of red spots!

Doctor: Do you feel hot?

Dot: No, I am not hot.

Nip: She just feels spotty!

Pip: **Red** and spotty.

Mum: Shush, pups!

Doctor: Nurse, please get us the green bone.

Nurse: Here you are, Dot. Chew this bone.

Dot: But it's a **green** bone!

Nip: Yuck! It looks bad!

Mum: Shush! Go on, Dot. Chew it!

Dot chews the bone.

Pip: Look! Look at Dot now!

Mum: All Dot's spots are **green**!

Nurse: Oh no!

Doctor: That was my best bone for spots.

Mum: But the best bone was no good.

Doctor: Um, let me look in my book …

Nip: That is a **big** book!

Doctor: Yes, but it cannot fix Dot's spots.

Nurse: Look in **this** book, Doctor Woof.

Dot: That book is very, very big!

Pip: I bet that book can fix Dot's spots!

Doctor: Let me see …

Mum: Oh! Look at Doctor Woof's nose!

Dot: Doctor Woof has a spot on his nose.

Nip: Yes, it's a big red spot!

Pip: And he has a big spot on his tail too!

Nurse: Oh no! Doctor Woof has got the spots from Dot!

Doctor: Yowl!

Pip: Look, Mum! Now Dot has no spots! No red spots and no green spots.

Mum: The green bone has got rid of them!

Dot: But look at Doctor Woof!

Nip: He has lots and lots of red spots!

Nurse: Oh no! What can we do? Dot has eaten up the last green bone!

Dot: I think Doctor Woof needs to go to the doctor too!

Doctor: Yowl!